C000176236

# Flute
# Grade 4

## Pieces
for Trinity College London exams

## 2017-2020

Published by
Trinity College London Press
www.trinitycollege.com

Registered in England
Company no. 09726123

Copyright © 2016 Trinity College London Press
First impression, June 2016

Printed in England by Caligraving Ltd.

# Siciliano

from *Sonata no. 2*

J S Bach
(1685–1750)

poco rit.

# After All

Adam Caird

8

# Piece no. 3

from *Celtic Collage*

Keri Degg
(b. 1975)

Reproduced from *Celtic Collage; 7 Original Celtic pieces for Flute and Piano*, by Keri Degg, published by Masquerade Music.

# Minuet

## from *The Wand of Youth, First Suite*

*Arr.* Trevor Wye

Edward Elgar
(1857–1934)

# Recuerdos de la Bahía

John Sands
(b. 1931)

# Tango Final

Astor Piazzolla
(1921–1992)